Urban wetlands
for nature conservation
and stormwater control

Prepared for the Nature Conservancy Council
by Stephen A Simmons and Ann Barker
of Midland Environment Ltd, 1988

Designed by Meridian Creative, Printed by W. Lake 1M.

The Nature Conservancy Council is the body responsible for advising Government on nature conservation in Great Britain. Its work includes the selection, establishment and management of National Nature Reserves; the selection and management of Marine Nature Reserves; the identification and notification of Sites of Special Scientific Interest; the provision of advice and dissemination of knowledge about nature conservation; and the support and conduct of research relevant to these functions.

This is one of a range of publications produced by Publicity Services Branch. A catalogue listing current titles is available from Dept UWA, Nature Conservancy Council, Northminster House, Peterborough PE1 1UA.

Contents

Amid growing national and international concern over the loss or despoilation of a variety of habitats, particular attention has been given to the plight of wetland plants and animals found in our rivers, ponds, fens, marshes and estuaries. These wetland communities are of immense importance for nature conservation. Many species are adapted to specific aquatic conditions and are particularly vulnerable to the effects of pollution, drainage, fluctuations in water tables and general disturbance. Changes in farming practices and the pressures on land in rural areas have caused a marked decline in the number, extent and quality of wetlands across much of rural Britain. For this reason it has become increasingly important to protect all existing wetland habitats and to consider ways to develop new wetland resources.

Although nature conservation has been seen traditionally as an activity confined to the countryside, there is now a growing movement towards the integration of measures to promote wildlife alongside all of our day-to-day activities. Many water authorities and local authorities are engaged in ambitious schemes to improve the quality of the environment for wildlife (10), – see References.

Activities to promote nature conservation are not limited to the countryside, nature in our towns and cities is important too. Modern techniques of urban stormwater management offer opportunities for the development of new wetland resources. The design and management of these fragile aquatic habitats will be vitally important if the full benefits for nature conservation are to be realised.

Characteristics of urban stormwater

Urban areas have a characteristic stormwater run-off regime which is a product of man's activities, the extremes of the city climate, density and forms of built development, settlement patterns in relation to natural drainage networks and the urban drainage system. When land is developed, the construction of buildings, pavements, roads and other impervious surfaces and the consequent loss of vegetation reduces the ground's storage capacity for rainfall and increases the rate and quantity of surface run-off. The construction of elaborate surface water collection systems and stormwater sewers further increases the rate at which surface water run-off

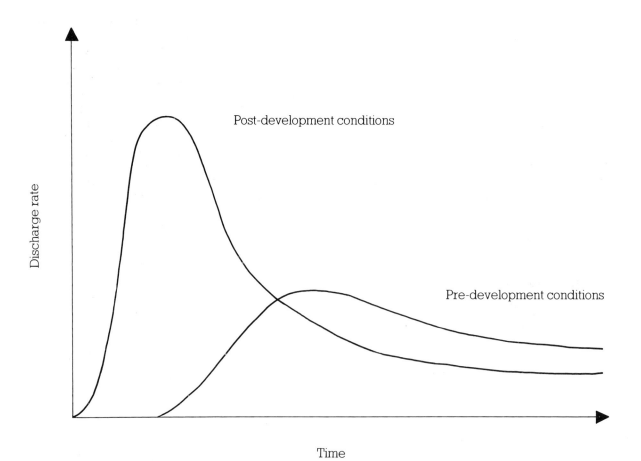

Urban development increases the volume and rate of surface run-off

4

reaches nearby water courses. Following heavy rainfall, abundant and rapid surface run-off may lead to high peak stream flows and consequent downstream flooding, during and immediately after the storm event. Water quality also deteriorates with increasing urbanisation as surface run-off carries with it increased loads of pollutants and sediments. Reduced surface infiltration lowers groundwater recharge rates. The resulting lower stream flows between storm events are frequently supplemented by the addition of waterborne wastes. Pollution deriving from sewage and industrial effluents further exacerbates water quality problems facing urban areas (6).

The need for stormwater control

Massive storm surges are not only dangerous to human life, they may also lead to a more frequent incidence of downstream flooding. Where housing and industrial developments have encroached onto urban flood plains, the control of flooding has become a major problem for municipal and river engineers. Solutions have often required extensive engineering works including flood alleviation channels, flood embankments and alteration of stream channels. These measures have a drastic impact on aquatic wildlife and wildlife habitat.

With a greater emphasis now being placed on the improvement of water quality in our urban water courses, more attention is being given to the possible hazards associated with pollution arising from stormwater discharges.

Rain falling onto a city performs a valuable function in helping to wash away much of the dirt and grime that has accumulated in the preceding dry period. By the time excess rainwater has washed over roofs, roads, and other impervious surfaces it will have become contaminated with numerous 'pollutants' which are then washed into the nearest water course through storm sewer systems. Researchers have found that stormwater may contain a wide variety of pollutants including:

☐ suspended solids,
☐ nutrients (nitrogen and phosphorus),
☐ toxins (including heavy metals such as lead and cadmium, and pesticides),
☐ bacteria, viruses and other pathogenic micro-organisms,
☐ oil and detergents,
☐ de-icing chemicals.

Suspended solids (small particles of organic debris and soil) are a major cause of stormwater quality degradation. The concentrations of suspended solids in urban run-off compare unfavourably with those in domestic sewage. Soil erosion arising from construction activities in particular, has been found to be a major cause of sediment related problems. Building construction in a small catchment in south-west England for example, was demonstrated in one study to increase levels of suspended sediments by 2 to 10 times, and occasionally up to 100 times those observed in the pre-construction state (12).

Erosion on this scale can have significant impact on the wildlife in receiving water courses by altering the structure and productivity of plant, invertebrate and vertebrate communities. Rapid settling of sediment can cover vital spawning grounds and bottom living invertebrates, while high concentrations of suspended sediments may increase scouring and erosion of stream channels and vegetation, reduce light penetration and limits the distance underwater predators can see.

Phosphorus and nitrogen are found in urban run-off. Owing to their importance as nutrients, in excess levels both may stimulate nuisance blooms of algae and promote unwanted growth of aquatic plants. Fertilizers used in parks and gardens are thought to be one of the sources of nutrients in urban run-off.

Toxins in urban run-off may include heavy metals, such as lead, zinc, cadmium, copper, nickel, mercury and arsenic; pesticides, such as Lindane and Chlordane; and a wide variety of organic chemicals. Heavy metals are by far the most significant pollutants in urban run-off. Lead and cadmium are of concern owing to their potential threat to the health of animals and in particular to man, while copper, nickel and zinc are all highly toxic to aquatic plants and animals. Sources of metals in urban run-off include vehicle exhaust emissions, metal corrosion, atmospheric deposition and industrial pollution.

Biochemical oxygen demand (BOD) is used as a measure of the amount of organic matter that is bacterially degradable. Levels of BOD in urban stormwater may be high, and in many instances will be comparable to those of secondary sewage treatment plant discharges. During the decay and decomposition of organic matter, micro-organisms take up oxygen from the water depleting the reserves of dissolved oxygen needed by fish and other aquatic organisms.

The above listing is by no means complete and depending on the nature of the catchment area, other water quality problems may be associated with urban stormwater including high levels of bacteria and pathogenic micro-organisms, de-icing salts, waste oils from road surfaces and DIY oil changes, spillage of industrial chemicals and odours.

Rural

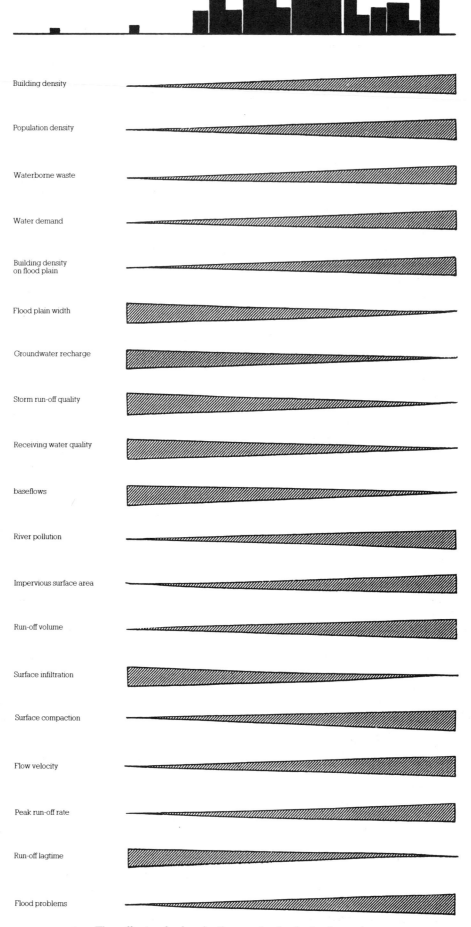

Building density

Population density

Waterborne waste

Water demand

Building density
on flood plain

Flood plain width

Groundwater recharge

Storm run-off quality

Receiving water quality

baseflows

River pollution

Impervious surface area

Run-off volume

Surface infiltration

Surface compaction

Flow velocity

Peak run-off rate

Run-off lagtime

Flood problems

The effects of urbanisation on the hydrologic cycle

The management of urban stormwater has traditionally been based on techniques which aim to maximise the rate at which surface run-off is removed from a catchment. In British towns and cities, stormwater is largely routed through 'combined' sewerage systems which are designed to cope with both domestic and surface water drainage. Overflows are constructed at points along the combined sewer network to cope with flows in excess of design capacity. More recent developments, particularly in some of the New Towns, have moved away from combined sewers in favour of separate sewer networks in which foul sewers and storm drains are kept apart. Separate storm sewers are usually routed directly to the nearest watercourse. These practices maximise the rate at which stormwater reaches streams increasing erosion, sedimentation and flooding problems downstream which often require extensive engineering solutions such as channel straightening and enlargement or the construction of flood relief channels.

With growing emphasis now being placed on the control of water quality and on reducing surface run-off volumes, engineers are turning towards practices which detain or retain stormwater close to the point where it fell. Many techniques have been pioneered including development of porous road surfaces, storing rainwater on rooftops and routing rainwater into grassed areas where it is allowed to soak away. By far the most widespread technique, however, is based on the construction of storage ponds (7). Two basic designs are in use. The first type is the 'dry' basin or detention basin which is designed to detain stormwater temporarily and empty slowly once the flood peak has passed. The other type is the 'wet' or retention pond where a body of permanent water is maintained with capacity for storage of stormwater above the normal level of the pool.

Both types of storage pond control the rate of discharge to receiving water courses and hence may be effective in helping to alleviate flood related problems. With increasing emphasis on the control of the quality as well as quantity of stormwater, efficiency in removing pollutants from stormwater has become an important factor. Researchers have found that while both designs may retain water for a sufficient length of time to allow some suspended sediments to settle out, retention ponds are generally more effective at removing pollutants than detention basins. One of the problems with the design of detention basins is that sediments deposited in previous storms may be re-suspended and washed from the basin by the next storm flow.

In contrast, retention ponds have been found to be highly effective in controlling run-off quality,

although design can have a bearing on performance. Researchers working in the United States for the Environmental Protection Agency's Nationwide Urban Run-off Programme (NURP) have found that pollutant removal efficiencies for water passing through ponds depends on the size of the permanent water area in relation to the area of the catchment and the characteristics of the storm. Results from the 14 retention ponds studied by NURP projects, indicate suspended particulate and lead removals in excess of 90% for adequately sized ponds. Pollutants which have greater solubility in urban run-off showed lower reductions of 65% for phosphorous and around 50% for organic matter (as indicated by BOD), nitrogen, zinc and copper. The researchers suggest that complex biological processes are important in helping to remove soluble pollutants such as the plant nutrients, nitrogen and phosphorous, which are taken up by phytoplankton and growing plants during the spring and summer and released again during the winter when the plants die (11).

Physical entrapment of pollutants onto particles of sediment deposited at the bottom of pools is another important mechanism for pollutant removal. This is particularly significant for heavy metals which may accumulate in pond sediments. It is possible that in certain circumstances the long-term build up of such toxic pollutants in sediments may represent a hazard to wildlife. It is also possible that the presence of toxic pollutants may present problems for the disposal of sediments removed from ponds during maintenance. The nature and scope of this threat is not well understood at present and will be the subject of future research.

Accumulation of sediments in retention ponds may also represent a maintenance commitment if water depths and design capacity are to be maintained. In large ponds, regular sediment removal at the inlet may be impractical.

With increasing awareness of the possible benefits that man-made retention pond systems may have on water quality, it has been widely suggested that natural or man-made marshes and other wetlands, may also act as sinks for pollutants in stormwater in a similar way. The biological processes involved in the treatment of urban run-off in wetlands are not well understood. Insufficient practical information is available to characterise general capabilities or to identify general design principles. Results from the few documented studies that are available look encouraging. Reductions in BOD (54-89%), suspended solids (94-99%) and heavy metals (up to 97%) have been reported (4). Results from a combined detention pond and wetland system in central Florida indicate reductions of 88%, 83%,

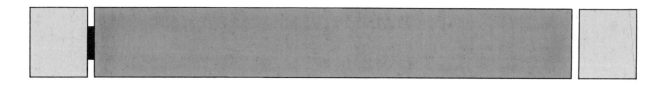

70%, 36% and 43% for suspended solids, lead, zinc, nitrogen and phosphorous respectively, for stormwater run-off passing through the system (9). It is increasingly clear, however, that our natural and semi-natural wetland habitats are highly susceptible to changes in nutrient status or fluctuations in water tables and therefore additional modifications to these valuable ecosystems may be undesirable.

Urban wetlands for stormwater control and nature conservation

While the primary impetus for constructing retention ponds is for their role in controlling the quantity and quality of urban run-off, wildlife too may benefit. The creation of new aquatic resources in urban and urbanizing areas will provide valuable opportunities for the development of wetland habitats which may help to offset some of the loss and despoilation of existing wetlands due to pollution, drainage and infilling. Experience has shown that in appropriate circumstances ponds can be designed to maximise their value for wildlife providing that both the habitat requirements and the constraints imposed by pollution are taken into account.

The most comprehensive investigations into the use of different stormwater control facilities by wildlife have taken place in the United States. In 1982, the National Institute for Urban Wildlife began a study of the city of Columbia to find out what aspects of the city's 9 detention basins, 22 retention ponds and 3 lakes were attractive for birds, amphibians, reptiles and mammals (2). Bird use of retention ponds was found to be more extensive than use of detention basins. Breeding waterfowl preferred smaller ponds to lakes. Use of shallow ponds (average depth 0.7 metres, with gently sloping sides) by breeding pairs of mallards was about 2.4 and 3.2 times greater than use of deeper ponds (2.1m average depth with steep sides) and lakes, respectively. Shallow ponds with less open water and more abundant aquatic vegetation were observed to provide better feeding sites and cover for wildlife. Shallow spits and bars of sediments were particularly attractive to wildlife (1). Migrating waterfowl like grebes and coots on the other hand preferred the larger ponds and lakes for resting and feeding. Other wetland birds, including herons, common snipe and sandpipers were more frequently recorded at shallow ponds. Permanent water empoundments were also found to be more attractive to amphibians, reptiles and mammals. In contrast detention basins which were frequently mown were less attractive to wildlife and provided little useful habitat. Some ground foraging species such as the starling were observed to feed in detention basins. Detention basins with streams were less frequently mown and the tall herbaceous vegetation was attractive to song sparrows who showed an affinity for the water's edge (2).

A Californian researcher reported that waterbird use of a man-made urban stormwater wetland in the Coyote Hills Regional Park was similar to waterbird use of a nearby natural wetland. Eighty-eight species of waterfowl and other waterbirds were recorded during the study. The shallow water and mudflat areas attracted the greatest diversity of waterbirds. Deeper open water attracted diving birds (5).

Similar success in creating attractive aquatic habitats within stormwater control facilities has also been achieved in this country. In the Sandwell Valley, West Midlands, for example, a retention basin has been constructed to balance stormwater flows in the nearby River Tame. The pool has been landscaped with islands, bays and other features to attract wildlife. Over 170 species of bird have been recorded including jacksnipe, wheatears, whinchats and marsh harriers. The area around the pools proves popular with people too. Over 30,000 people a year visit the Sandwell Valley to enjoy watching and learning about the wildlife. A nature centre run by the Royal Society for the Protection of Birds provides a unique opportunity for schools and other groups to study nature at the heart of the West Midlands conurbation.

In attempting to develop wildlife habitat on stormwater control ponds and wetlands, pollution deriving from urban run-off may impose constraints on what can or should be achieved. As we have seen in the earlier sections of this publication, urban stormwater may contain numerous pollutants, many of which can be toxic to plants and animals. Therefore, in situations where pollution levels are likely to be particularly high, it may be inadvisable to encourage wildlife use of retention ponds or other wetlands without some kind of water treatment for inflowing stormwater. Examples of the circumstances in which pollution could represent a potential limitation include: locations downstream of combined sewer overflows, industrial areas, sites mainly receiving highway run-off, and areas likely to be directly affected by oil pollution.

Improved transport has enabled more urban dwellers to have access to the countryside surrounding our towns and cities, but many still have poor access to natural and semi-natural areas where they can relax from the stresses and rigours of day-to-day urban life. Measures which create new semi-natural greenspaces in the environment where people live, will therefore be of considerable benefit to local communities. Wetlands in particular have considerable aesthetic, recreational and educational value. In seeking to make stormwater control facilities more attractive to wildlife, they will also be made more attractive to people. It is likely that support for stormwater management will be increased if aesthetic considerations and the views of the public are taken into account.

The National Institute for Urban Wildlife have surveyed people's attitudes towards different types of stormwater control facilities in Columbia, Maryland, USA. Many residents used the local retention ponds for walking, bicycle riding, birdwatching and general enjoyment of nature. Retention ponds were preferred by 75% of local house-owners. Only 17% preferred dry detention basins. As a measure of the attraction of wetland areas, 73% said that they would pay more for a property located in a neighbourhood with a retention pond designed to encourage wildlife. The majority reported that they enjoyed watching birds and other wildlife on the ponds. Although some residents did express concern about possible nuisances, hazards and maintenance, the benefits were considered to outweigh these negative aspects (3).

With increasing land prices and higher building costs, land set aside for stormwater management may represent an added cost for housing and commercial developments. At the Aztec West commercial estate near Bristol, the construction of stormwater retention ponds was seen as an opportunity to enhance the aesthetic character of the estate rather than as an additional cost burden. Set amidst extensive landscape planting, the ponds are now attractive features both for companies located on the estate and for local wildlife. Indeed the ponds have been so successful that the managers of Aztec West are considering including similar features in future developments.

By designing stormwater management facilities to control water quality, enhance local habitats and provide access for nearby residents, planners and engineers may help to improve the quality of the urban environment significantly for wildlife and people.

Urban development will always affect the environment. Built development has particularly adverse consequences on the streams and rivers draining our towns and cities. In attempting to limit or prevent damage due to pollution, erosion or flooding, authorities have traditionally relied on extensive engineering solutions which have a drastic impact on wildlife and wildlife habitat. Current emphasis is placed on reducing pollution and flooding by permanently or temporarily holding back precipitation where it falls. Detention basins and retention ponds are increasingly used to balance stormwater run-off from new developments. Detention basins are normally dry, only containing water for short periods during heavy rainfall. These offer little potential for creation of wildlife habitat. Retention ponds on the other hand maintain a permanent body of water which can be used to provide a new aquatic habitat which benefits both wildlife and people.

Guidelines governing the design criteria for stormwater detention and retention ponds (7) and on river engineering practices which allow for the needs of wildlife (8 & 10) are already available to planners and engineers. The following considerations should also be taken into account in the design of retention ponds and other wetlands in order to optimise their value for wildlife

☐ Man-made wetlands can and should be created in urban and urbanising areas as a functional part of stormwater management. Permanent wetland habitats can contribute to the control of both quantity and quality of urban run-off as well as enhancing the urban environment for both man and wildlife.

☐ All potential locations for ponds and other wetlands must be evaluated to select the most appropriate site. Factors to be considered include the nature of the catchment, likely sources of pollution, the needs of local communities, physical and ecological opportunities and constraints.

☐ Enhancement of stormwater control ponds for wildlife should only be considered at locations where water quality is unlikely to affect adversely plants and animals attracted to the site.

☐ Locations likely to be affected by discharges from combined sewers or other identifiable sources of pollutants should be avoided unless suitable water treatment can be provided.

☐ The Nature Conservancy Council must be consulted about all proposed schemes which may affect a Site of Special Scientific Interest and should also be consulted on other sites of importance to nature conservation. Where possible, ponds should be located in areas where disturbance to valuable existing habitats by future construction activities can be avoided or kept to a minimum.

☐ Stormwater retention ponds must be designed to meet appropriate standards, including legal requirements. Enhancement for wildlife should be incorporated into the design stage and not added as an afterthought.

☐ Oil, sediment and litter traps may be required at the inlets to some ponds. These should be designed to cause minimum intrusion and facilitate regular access for maintenance.

☐ To minimise disturbance to wildlife, at least part of the pond should be relatively inaccessible to people visiting the site. Landscaping with shrub woodland will provide cover and help to deter the casual visitor.

☐ Ponds should be designed with spits and promontories which break up straight shorelines and give shelter and seclusion for wildlife. Islands are recommended for larger pools. These will help to direct water flows throughout the pond, increasing the time it remains there and its oxygenation, and will provide natural refuges for animals and plants which will be free from disturbance.

☐ Water depths should not exceed 60cm for 25-50% of the water surface area, with around 50-75% having a depth of not less than 1-1.4m. An emergent vegetation/open water ratio of 50:50 should be maintained.

☐ Banks should be gently sloping to facilitate colonisation by emergent plants. A side slope of between 10:1 and 20:1 is more beneficial to wildlife than steeper slopes. They are also safer for children who may be attracted to the water's edge. The transition between deeper and shallower areas will suit a range of different vegetation types.

☐ Given the right conditions natural colonisation of ponds will take place over time. This process can be speeded up by planting of appropriate marginal, emergent and floating plants. Species should be selected from those which are local to the area, are capable of withstanding fluctuations in water levels and are less susceptible to the effects of pollution. Examples of pollution tolerant species include: fennel pondweed, *Potomageton pectinatus,* reedmace, *Typha latifolia,* common reed, *Phragmites australis* and water forget-me-not, *Myosotis scorpioides.* Introduction of species which have no history of occurrence in the general area should not be carried out without

expert opinion being sought or without examination in the light of the requirements of the Wildlife and Countryside Act 1981.

☐ Long-term management plans should be prepared to guide future maintenance and development of habitats within the area of the pool. Management should be planned to cause least possible disturbance.

☐ Build-up of sediments around the inlets to the pool will lead to the formation of spits and bars which are of great value to wildlife. Over time however, sediment accumulation may reduce water depths and necessitate dredging. Sediment removal should be timed to cause minimum disturbance to wildlife and should be undertaken in stages over several years to allow recolonisation from the undisturbed areas. Plants removed during maintenance should be transplanted wherever possible. Spoil should be deposited well away from the pool's edge to prevent nutrients and pollutants, such as heavy metals, leaching back into the water. Sediments containing high levels of pollution should be disposed of safely.

☐ Access to the pond for quiet recreational and educational purposes should be encouraged wherever possible. Water contact activities, such as pond dipping, should be discouraged at sites where bacterial contamination can present a risk to health.

As experience grows, the conservation-conscious engineer will learn to recognise new opportunities for promoting wildlife within stormwater management schemes. This requires creativity and ingenuity, together with an awareness of the needs of different plant and animal communities.

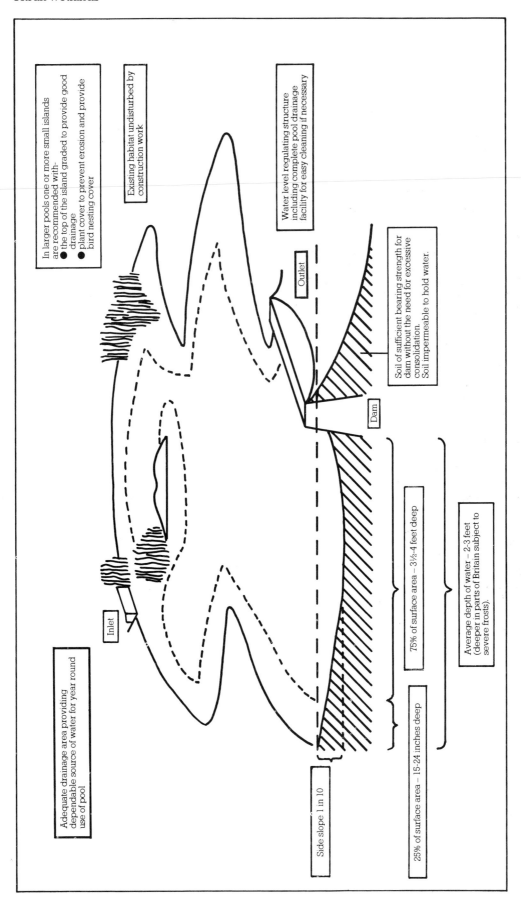

In larger pools one or more small islands are recommended with-
● the top of the island graded to provide good drainage
● plant cover to prevent erosion and provide bird nesting cover

Existing habitat undisturbed by construction work

Water level regulating structure including complete pool drainage facility for easy cleaning if necessary

Outlet

Soil of sufficient bearing strength for dam without the need for excessive consolidation.
Soil impermeable to hold water.

Dam

75% of surface area – 3½-4 feet deep

Average depth of water – 2-3 feet (deeper in parts of Britain subject to severe frosts).

Side slope 1 in 10

25% of surface area – 15-24 inches deep

Inlet

Adequate drainage area providing dependable source of water for year round use of pool

Summary of design criteria for wildlife enhancement in detention ponds

Acknowledgements

This publication could not have been produced
without the valuable cooperation of the following
organisations-

Anglian Water Authority
Northumbrian Water Authority
North-West Water Authority
Severn-Trent Water Authority
Southern Water Authority
South-West Water Authority
Thames Water Authority
Welsh Water Authority
Wessex Water Authority
Yorkshire Water Authority
Water Research Centre

and the many researchers who contributed to this
project.

References

1 ADAMS, L.W., L.E. DOVE & T.M. FRANKLIN. 1985. Mallard pair and brood use of urban stormwater-control impoundments. *Wildlife Society Bulletin (U.S.) 13*, pp 46-51.

2 ADAMS, L.W., T.M. FRANKLIN, L.E. DOVE & J.M. DUFFIELD. 1985. *Design Considerations for Wildlife in Urban Stormwater Management.* Transactions 51st N.A. Wildlife & Natural Resources Conference.

3 ADAMS, L.W., L.E. DOVE & D.L. LEEDY. 1984. Public attitudes toward urban wetlands for stormwater control and wildlife enhancement. *Wildlife Society Bulletin (U.S.), 12.* pp 299-303.

4 CHAN, E., T.A. BURSZTYNSKY, N. HANTZSCHE & Y.J. LITWIN. 1981. *The Use of Wetlands for Water Pollution Control.* Municipal Environmental Research Laboratory, U.S. Environmental Protection Agency, Ohio.

5 DUFFIELD, J.M. 1986. Waterbird use of an urban stormwater wetland system in Central California, USA. *Colonial Waterbirds, 9, 2,* pp 227-235.

6 HALL, M.J. 1984. *Urban Hydrology.* Elsevier Applied Science Publishers.

7 HALL, M.J. & D.L. HOCKIN. 1980. Guide to the 'design' of storage ponds for flood control in partly urbanised catchment areas. *Technical Note 100, July.* Construction Industry Research and Information Association.

8 LEWIS, G. & G. WILLIAMS. 1984. *Rivers and Wildlife Handbook: A guide to practices which further the conservation of wildlife on rivers.* RSPB.

9 MARTIN, E.H. & R.A. MILLER. 1987. Efficiency of an urban stormwater detention system. *Proceedings of the 4th International Conference on Urban Storm Drainage,* pp 143-148. Lausanne.

10 NEWBOLD, C., J. PURSEGLOVE & N. HOLMES. 1983. *Nature conservation and river engineering.* Nature Conservancy Council.

11 U.S. E.P.A. 1983. Results of the nationwide urban run-off program. *Vol. 1 – Final Report.* U.S. Environmental Protection Agency, Washington D.C.

12 WALLING, D.E. & K.J. GREGORY. 1970. The measurement of the effects of building construction on drainage basin dynamics. *Journal of Hydrology, 11,* pp 128-144.